Latino Poetry

GLOBE FEARON
EDUCATIONAL PUBLISHER

PARAMUS, NEW JERSEY

Paramount Publishing

Photographic Interpretations Made by the Following Students:

Mike Caraballo: p. 84.
Cyndi Cartagena: p. 5, 28, 31, 34, 61, 71, 77, 81.
Jeffrey Gamble: p. 67.
B. Elisa Garcia: p. 2, 13, 33, 38–39.
Juanita Hesonas: 42.
Luis Lara: p. 17, 46.
Richard Rose: p. 51, 87.
Robert Ruiz: p. 10, 23, 55.
Nadia Voukitchevitch: 57.

Print acknowledgments can be found on pages 119 and 120.

Executive Editor: Virginia Seeley
Senior Editor: Barbara Levadi
Project Editor: Karen Bernhaut
Contributing Editor: Jacqueline M. Kiraithe-Córdova
Production Editor: June Bodansky
Art Director: Nancy Sharkey
Cover Design: Joan Jacobus
Production Manager: Penny Gibson
Production Coordinator: Walter Niedner
Desktop Specialist: José A. López
Marketing Managers: Sandra Hutchison and Elmer Ildefonso
Photo Research: Jenifer Hixson
Cover Photo: Cyndi Cartagena.

Printed in the United States of America
8 9 10   02 01

ISBN 0-835-90726-0

GLOBE FEARON
EDUCATIONAL PUBLISHER
PARAMUS, NEW JERSEY

Paramount Publishing

CONTENTS

UNIT FOUR

Familiar Landscapes: Places Called Home *48*

UNIT FIVE

The Family: Honoring Loved Ones *59*

Insights: Understanding Ourselves, Appreciating Others

ABOUT THE BOOK

This book of poetry is for you, the young adult of today. It is designed to help you appreciate poetry, and at the same time, bring you closer to the experiences of Latinos in this country. The Latino community includes people from a variety of cultures; Latinos may be of Chicano, Puerto Rican, Cuban, or Dominican heritage, among others. This book will introduce you to the rich and varied experiences of Latinos from all these cultures throughout the United States. You will read the works of some of the best-known Latino and Latina poets of today, such as Lorna Dee Cervantes, Gary Soto, Victor Hernández Cruz, Tato Laviera, and Sandra María Esteves. As you read their poetry, allow yourself to become part of their worlds.

ABOUT THE THEMES

You will notice that the poetry in this book is organized by theme. This arrangement is intended to capture a wide range of experiences. The themes reflect the joys and hardships of the Latino community. They give voice to people who have faced conflicts and challenges, but who have also celebrated pride, happiness, and love. The themes show what is special about being Latino. They also present values and concerns that are common to all people, regardless of their culture. As you read the poems, try to recognize the unique as well as the universal elements in the themes.

THE POETRY AND YOU

The poems in this book reflect both the positive and negative aspects of Latino life. Through this poetry, you will experience the hardships that Latinos have faced. You will read about the hopes and disappointments of immigrants and the struggles of migrant farmworkers. You will also learn about the values and traditions of the Latino cultures, such as the importance of family, community, and heritage.

At the same time, you will discover that these poems are about you because they often reflect the experiences of all people, not just Latinos. After reading Victor Hernández Cruz's "Side 32," you may experience the feeling of happiness that comes from just being yourself. After reading Lorna Dee Cervantes's "The Beauty of Me and My People," you may experience a sense of pride in your own cultural heritage. Through the poets' musical phrases and powerful images, you will come to better understand yourself and your world.

ABOUT THE PHOTOGRAPHS

The photographs used in this book were taken by students just like you. Globe Fearon went to several high schools to find photography students who might be interested in taking pictures for the book. To our delight, we found many students who were very enthusiastic about participating in the project.

Each student was given a group of poems. After reading and discussing the poems, the students set out with their cameras to shoot their interpretations. They tried to capture the emotions and moods reflected in the poems. They took pictures of subjects some might consider commonplace, such as their friends, homes, and neighborhood streets. Yet, these ordinary scenes helped bring the poems to life.

As the last photos were completed, we, the editors at Globe Fearon, and the students felt a great sense of accomplishment. The students were proud of their work, and we were awed by their talent. Our shared experience of making a book of poetry proved to be fun and worthwhile for everyone involved!

SEEKING A NEW LIFE: CONFLICTS AND CHALLENGES

Immigrants

PAT MORA

wrap their babies in the American flag,
feed them mashed hot dogs and apple pie,
name them Bill and Daisy,
buy them blonde dolls that blink blue
eyes or a football and tiny cleats
before the baby can even walk,
speak to them in thick English,
      hallo, babee, hallo,
whisper in Spanish or Polish
when the babies sleep, whisper
in the dark parent bed, that dark
parent fear, "Will they like
our boy, our girl, our fine american
boy, our fine american girl?"

A New Refugee

MARISELLA VEIGA

stands
outside my door this morning.
He is an exterminator,
wanting to work.
He is from Havana,[1]
(our province),
with no regrets about having left.

I've seen him
selling limes and newspapers,
I've seen him pushing carts
with snowcones,
I have seen his bent shoulders,
him eating beneath a tree
with a hunger that is not
from here.

Countryman. Stranger.
You are my father twenty years ago.
Come in. Have lunch. In this house
we are not without a gun.

---

1. Havana (huh-VAHN-uh) the capital of Cuba

People of the Harvest

NAOMI QUIÑÓNEZ

The crushed grape
withers on the vine
no gnarled hands to pick it
no one to make wine.
Lettuce now lost
wilts on its row
the empty fields forgotten
by scythe* and sickle* and hoe.
Cotton worms slowly
drying in the sun
if there were backs
to carry it
but there are none.
Fruit long past ripe
falls heavy to the ground
and bursts its rotting entrails*
with a sluggish* sound.
The fields are all in mourning
rotting blackly
in their sorrow
for the people of the harvest
who will not return tomorrow.
The grapevine now a gravemark
for every back-wrenched soul
that spent a life of labor
and died
giving birth to growth.

_____

* These terms are defined in the glossary.

The poison that protects the field
often kills the worker.
The sun that ignites
orchards to bloom
beats hard upon the child
and sucks life away.
When the field has finished rotting
and gives herself to bloom
be aware of the many souls
in the orchard's perfume
in the fine green skin of the plant
in the sweetness of the fruit
in the soil dark
with my people's blood
in the fiber
of the root.

The Maestro's Barber Shop

RICARDO VÁSQUEZ

Next to the Apostolic Church of God,
crossing the street where the Catholic church was located,
was the barber shop of the maestro*
where my father went to have his hair cut.
All the old acquaintances arrived during the morning
greeting one another like the friends they were
the barrio¹ aristocracy,* men of
wisdom and of dreams, Lucky Lager instead
of Mint Juleps.
The Maestro with the same face every Saturday;
strong, round, some teeth missing, but kept smiling,
the great listener, with noble hands
worth gold entangled in their hair.
Dreams of better things to come were a reality
in the maestro's barber shop.
There over the mirror, a photograph of the
García boy who pitched for the
Cleveland Indians was the confirmation.

---

1. **barrio** (BAHR-ee-oh) *adj.* neighborhood

* These terms are defined in the glossary.

Mestizo[1]

LUIS OMAR SALINAS

I

We have walked for miles
Without water or food to your church
America
      how about getting us a bus
and some food and water
or we'll burn the
   church down

II

In the fields
   and in the barrios[2]
our
   Mestizos
are fed up with conditions/
and we believe
in our man from Delano*
     César Chávez[3]
because the rich man
has put us down
     for many years/

---

1. *Mestizo* (mehs-TEE-zoh) *n.* a person of mixed background, usually of Indian and Spanish heritages

2. barrios (BAHR-ee-ohz) *n. pl.* neighborhoods

3. César Chávez (SEH-sahr CHA-ves) the organizer of the first agricultural unions for field workers that formed in the central valley of California

* This term is defined in the glossary.

so when you hear Huelga[4]
watch it
                'cause we're on our way/

III
In the fields
and in the barrios
                Mestizos
are singing songs

IV
Let's help our Mestizos
                America
        It's about time
                No?

V
Our color is brown
our blood
                comes from the Spanish
the Aztec[5]
and the Mayan[6]
        we had a great empire once
                we are rich in tradition
and we know what it is to suffer.

---

4. Huelga (WEHL-gah) *n.* a labor strike

5. Aztec (AZ-tehk) *n.* one of the great Indian civilizations of Mexico

6. Mayan (MAH-yuhn) *n.* one of the great Indian civilizations of Mexico

In a Farmhouse

LUIS OMAR SALINAS

Fifteen miles
out of Robstown*
with the Texas sun
fading in the distance
I sit in the bedroom
profoundly,
animated by the day's work
in the cottonfields.

I made two dollars and
thirty cents today
I am eight years old
and I wonder
how the rest of the Mestizos[1]
do not go hungry
and if one were to die
of hunger
what an odd way
to leave for heaven.

---

1. Mestizos (mehs-TEE-zohs) *n. pl.* people of mixed backgrounds, usually of
Indian and Spanish heritages

* This term is defined in the glossary.

Working Hands

FRANCISCO X. ALARCÓN

we clean
your room

we do
your dishes

a footnote
for you

but hands
like these

one day
will write

the main text
of this land

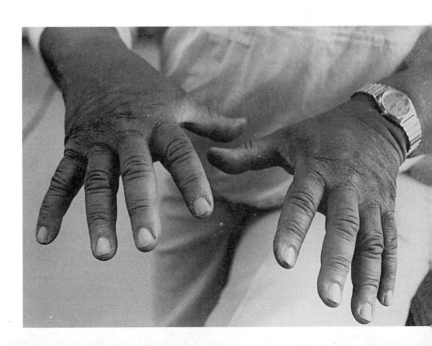

On heroes

HEBERTO PADILLA

Heroes
are always hoped for, waited for,
because they move in secret
and upset the order of things.
One fine day they appear,
exhausted and hoarse,
riding a tank,
dusty from the road,
clattering with their boots.
Heroes do not discuss;
rather, they lay excited
plans for tomorrow's life.
Heroes tell us what to do
and appoint us, to the world's astonishment.
They even hand to us
their role as Immortals.
They wrestle with our solitude
and our diatribes.*
In their way, they adjust the terror.
And finally, they impose* on us
abounding hope.

---

* These term is defined in the glossary.

REFLECTIONS: REMEMBERING PEOPLE AND PLACES

My Mother's Homeland

BELKIS CUZA MALÉ
Translated by Pamela Carmell

My mother always said
your homeland is any place,
preferably the place where you die.
That's why she bought the most arid* land,
the saddest landscape,
the driest grass,
and beside the wretched tree
began to build her homeland.
She built it by fits and starts
     (one day this wall, another day the roof;
from time to time, holes to let air squeeze in).
My house, she would say, is my homeland,
and I would see her close her eyes
like a young girl full of dreams
while she chose, once again, groping,
the place where she would die.

---

* This term is defined in the glossary.

We Live by What We See at Night

for my father

MARTÍN ESPADA

When the mountains of Puerto Rico[1]
flickered in your sleep
with a moist green light,
when you saw green bamboo* hillsides
before waking to East Harlem* rooftops
or Texas barracks,
when you crossed the bridge
built by your grandfather
over a river glimpsed
only in interrupted dreaming,
the craving for that island birthplace
burrowed,* deep
as thirty years' exile,
constant as your pulse.

This was the inheritance
of your son, born in New York:
that years before
I saw Puerto Rico,
I saw the mountains
looming above the projects,
overwhelming Brooklyn,
living by what I saw at night,
with my eyes closed.

---

1. Puerto Rico (PWEHR-tuh REE-koh) a territory of the United States located in the Caribbean

* These terms are defined in the glossary.

La Casa[1]

ROSEMARY CATACALOS

The house by the *acequia*,[2]
its front porch dark and
cool with begonias,
an old house, always there,
always of the same adobe,[3]
always full of the same lessons.
We would like to stop.
We know we belonged there once.
Our mothers are inside.
All the mothers are inside,
lighting candles, swaying
back and forth on their knees,
begging The Virgin's forgiveness
for having reeled us out
on such very weak string.
They are afraid for us.
They know we will not stop.
We will only wave as we pass by.
They will go on praying
that we might be simple again.

---

1. *La Casa* (lah KAH-sah) *n.* the house
2. *acequia* (ah-SEH-kyah) *n.* an irrigation ditch or canal
3. **adobe** (uh-DOH-bee) *n.* sun-dried brick

Granizo[1]

LEROY QUINTANA

To have been gone so long
But to have forgotten hail,
its name in Spanish, *granizo*,
until a storm, as I drove
toward a place named Golondrinas,[2]
eight miles from the main highway
because I was enchanted by the name
I was home again,
if only for a while, after eighteen years
I remembered grandfather, his cornfield
Somehow granizo belongs to him
He named it each summer
as he sat and watched, defined its terror
An old enemy, the way only water,
if it isn't gentle rain, can be

---

1. *Granizo* (grah-NEE-soh) *n.* hail
2. **Golondrinas** (goh-lohn-DREE-nahs) literally meaning "swallows," here the name of a town

The Latin Deli

JUDITH ORTIZ COFER

Presiding over a Formica* counter,
plastic Mother and Child magnetized
to the top of an ancient register,
the heady* mix of smells from the open bins
of dried codfish, the green plantains*
hanging in stalks like votive* offerings,
she is the Patroness of Exiles,*
a woman of no-age who was never pretty,
who spends her days selling canned memories
while listening patiently to the Puerto Ricans complain
that it would be cheaper to fly to San Juan[1]
than to buy a pound of Bustelo[2] coffee here,
and to Cubans perfecting their speech
of a "glorious return" to Havana[3]—where no one
has been allowed to die and nothing to change until then;
to Mexicans who pass through, talking lyrically*
of *dólares*[4] to be made in El Norte[5]—

---

1. **San Juan** (sahn HWAHN) the capital of Puerto Rico
2. **Bustelo** (boos-TEH-loh) *n.* a brand of coffee
3. **Havana** (huh-VAN-uh) the capital of Cuba
4. *dólares* (DOH-lah-res) *n. pl.* dollars
5. **El Norte** (el NOHR-teh) literally meaning "the north," a phrase commonly used in Mexico to refer to the United States

* These terms are defined in the glossary.

all wanting the comfort
of spoken Spanish, to gaze upon the family portrait
of her plain wide face, her ample bosom
resting on her plump arms, her look of maternal interest
as they speak to her and each other
of their dreams and their disillusions—
how she smiles understanding,
when they walk down the narrow aisles of her store
reading the labels of packages aloud, as if
they were the names of lost lovers: *Suspiros*,[6]
Merengues,[7] the stale candy of everyone's childhood.
                                    She spends her days
slicing *jamón y queso*[8] and wrapping it in wax paper
tied with string: plain ham and cheese
that would cost less at the A&P, but it would not satisfy
the hunger of the fragile old man lost in the folds
of his winter coat, who brings her lists of items
that he reads to her like poetry, or the others,
whose needs she must divine,* conjuring* up products
from places that now exist only in their hearts—
closed ports she must trade with.

---

6. **Suspiros** (soos-PEE-rohs) *n. pl.* kinds of candy

7. **Merengues** (meh-REN-ges) *n. pl.* kinds of candy made with egg whites

8. *jamón y queso* (hah-MOHN ee KEH-soh) ham and cheese

* These terms are defined in the glossary.

Coffee Bloom

AURORA LEVINS MORALES

In my country
the coffee blooms between hurricanes
fragile white blossoms that a raindrop could trample into
   the mud
a delicacy of lace
a hoax* of helplessness smothering up the wiry wood
   within.

On the hillside, deep in the rainforest
is a bush gone wild fifty years ago
its root as thick as my arm.
Here in the green shadows we whisper, the bush and I,
   our secret,
that hidden root
the reason we don't tremble, though the bruised petals
   flail*
no matter how wildly the wet wind blows.

---

* These terms are defined in the glossary.

jíbaro[1]

TATO LAVIERA

end of spring harvest,
el jíbaro mathematically
working the sun's energies,
nurturing every fruit to
blossom perfectly,
singing about
earth, la tierra,[2]
time after time, acre after acre,
year after year, the land provided.
end of spring harvest,
el jíbaro's guitar
on la carreta,[3]
pulling, ploughing slowly
towards sunset,
towards la cena,[4]
towards the afternoon breeze,
land, love, moon,
the lyrics emerged,
décimas[5] in place,
the ever-present "lo le lo lai,"[6]
and then, the song,
canción.[7]

---

1. *jíbaro* (HEE-bah-roh) *n.* the peasant or poor farmer of Puerto Rico
2. **la tierra** (lah TYEH-rrah) *n.* the land
3. **la carreta** (lah kah-RREH-tah) *n.* the cart or wagon
4. **la cena** (lah SEH-nah) *n.* the evening meal
5. **décimas** (DEH-see-mahs) *n. pl.* country ballads
6. **lo le lo lai** (loh leh loh leye) musical syllables commonly used in songs from the Caribbean
7. **canción** (kan-SYOHN) *n.* song

December's Picture

ANTONIA QUINTANA PIGÑO

He wondered why
his sister had sent
the calendar.
Maybe you'd like
to frame December?

Under oil gray skies
brown adobe[1] walls
stand silent
trimmed with snow.

Era la casa de tus abuelos.[2]

Curved earth walls flank
steps to a rooftop where
once a profusion* of chiles[3] lay
like warm red tiles in the sun.
Beyond ribboned windows of iron
whorls*—a possibility of lace
and somewhere
a chimney sends
scents of warmth
and roasting pinones.[4]

---

   1. adobe (uh-DOH-bee) *n.* sun-dried brick
   2. *Era la casa de tus abuelos.* (EH-rah lah KAH-sah deh toos ah-BWEH-lohs) It was the house of your grandparents.
   3. chiles (CHEE-les) *n. pl.* chiles; peppers
   4. pinones (pee-NYOH-nes) *n. pl.* pine nuts; small, edible seeds
   * These terms are defined in the glossary.

This was the house of our abuelos.[5]

He watched his mother
shape the tortilla[6]
her floured hands turning
the widening white circle.
He wondered if
she gave away her silks
her laces
and taking leave
touched the leaves
the branches
smooth walls of adobe
which enclosed
her father's garden,
if she turned and moved slowly
across the Old Town Bridge
to be with the young coal miner
from Madrid.
He wondered and thought to ask
but saw
already in her eyes
the silence of winter snow.

---

5. abuelos (ah-BWEH-lohs) *n. pl.* grandparents

6. tortilla (tohr-TEE-uh) *n.* thin, flat cornmeal bread shaped like a pancake

My Grandmother Would Rock Quietly and Hum

LEONARD ADAMÉ

in her house
she would rock quietly and hum
until her swelled hands
calmed

in summer
she wore thick stockings
sweaters
and grey braids

(when "el cheque"[1] came
we went to Payless
and I laughed greedily
when given a quarter)

mornings,
sunlight barely lit
the kitchen
and where
there were shadows
it was not cold

---

1. el cheque (el CHEH-keh) *n.* the check

she quietly rolled
flour tortillas[2] —
the "papas"[3]
cracking in hot lard
would wake me

she had lost her teeth
and when we ate
she had bread
soaked in "café"[4]

always her eyes
were clear
and she could see
as I cannot yet see—
through her eyes
she gave me herself

she would sit
and talk
of her girlhood—
of things strange to me:
    México
    epidemics*
    relatives shot
    her father's hopes
    of this country—
how they sank
with cement dust
to his insides

---

  2. tortillas (tohr-TEE-uhs) *n. pl.* thin, flat cornmeal bread shaped like pancakes

  3. papas (PAH-pahs) *n. pl.* potatoes

  4. café (kah-FEH) *n.* coffee

* This term is defined in the glossary.

now
when I go
to the old house
the worn spots
by the stove
echo of her shuffling
and
México
still hangs in her
fading
calendar pictures

IDENTITY: BALANCING TWO CULTURES

Applying for a Civil Service Job

MARIO GARZA

I would like to apply
    for a civil service job
You cannot apply!
    —Why not?
You have to be a veteran!
    —I'm a veteran
You still cannot apply!
    —Why not?
You have to have been out
    less than 120 days!
I just got out
    last month.
You still cannot apply!
    —Why not?
You need to be a
    Viet Nam Veteran!
I was in Viet Nam
    for 18 months.
You still cannot apply!
    —Why not?
You have to have been
    awarded a Purple Heart!*

---

* This term is defined in the glossary.

Would you believe
    three Purple Hearts!
You still cannot apply!
    —Why not?
You need to be able
    to walk on water!
What? With all these
        bullet holes,
            I'd sink!!

The Space Between

ANA LUISA ORTIZ DE MONTELLANO

"I'm a runaway child
        left Spanish behind."
The long grasp of its syllables holds
me like chewing gum on a shoe.†

I choose Spanish;
choose to live in the middle of the stream.
In the middle of the stream my feet like ears
feel the rush of water on the craft.
Each stick, each rock, each bottle cap
scrapes its skeletal* sign†

        The maze of marks that look so foreign
        strains my eyes. They are my own
        "King's English,"* the one I long denied.
        I speak their sounds that carry me
        into the air and giggle like a drum beat
        full of bees or a house of carts children
        peep round to look into the mirror
        where they set their palms
        against those of the mother
        who turns.

† This stanza has been translated from Spanish.

* These terms are defined in the glossary.

Nochebuena[1]

ROSARIO CAICEDO

Where I come from we have no snow
or winter solstice* or sleigh rides.
There are no fireplaces to roast
chestnuts at nights.

---

1. Nochebuena (noh-cheh-BWEH-nah) *n.* Christmas Eve
* This term is defined in the glossary.

We have the sun all around,
a sun that shines immediately
after those heavy rains when trees fall
and people from the slums drown.

After the deaths, always the sun—
not giving families the right
to have a gray day to mourn.
I remember funerals on sunny days
and Christmas Eves
where children, barefoot,
played with water.
Christmas Eve
Nochebuena: the good night.

I have forgotten the Christmas carols
that I memorized as a child
and cannot follow my daughter's voice
when she sings in a language
that I learned alone in an apartment
with a dictionary, the newspaper,
and the television always on.

And now after Halloween and Thanksgiving,
my children's Christmas comes.
Their laughter is heard in this big house
that in December has a decorated tree
and painted snowflakes on the walls.
They say that Santa Claus is coming.

Sometimes I feel
that I've been left
with nothing.

piñones[1]

LEROY QUINTANA

when i was young
we would sit by
an old firewood stove
watching my grandmother make candy,
listening to the stories
my grandparents would tell
about "the old days"
                      and eat piñones

now we belong
to a supersonic age
and have college degrees.
we sit around color t.v. sets
watching the super bowl
listening to howard cosell,
stories of rioting, war, inflation
                      and eat piñones

---

1. piñones (pee-NYOH-nes) *n. pl.* pine nuts; small, edible seeds

Side 12

VICTOR HERNÁNDEZ CRUZ

Manhattan dance Latin
In Spanish to African rhythms
A language lesson
Without opening your mouth

Here

SANDRA MARÍA ESTEVES

I am two parts/a person
boricua[1]/spic*
past and present
alive and oppressed
given a cultural beauty
. . . and robbed of a cultural identity

I speak the alien tongue
in sweet boriqueño[2] thoughts
know love mixed with pain
have tasted spit on ghetto stairways
. . . here, it must be changed
we must change it

I may never overcome
the theft of my isla[3] heritage
dulce palmas de coco[4] on Luquillo[5]
sway in windy recesses I can only imagine
and remember how it was

But that reality now a dream
teaches me to see, and will
bring me back to me.

---

1. **boricua** (boh-REE-kwah) *n.* a person from Puerto Rico
2. **boriqueño** (boh-ree-KEH-nyoh) *adj.* of or from Puerto Rico
3. **isla** (EES-lah) *adj.* island
4. **dulce palmas de coco** (DOOL-seh PAHL-mahs deh KOH-koh) sweet coconut palm trees
5. **Luquillo** (loo-KEE-yoh) *n.* a regional term meaning Puerto Rico; a part of Puerto Rico

* This term is defined in the glossary.

Little Sister Born in This Land

to Vicky

ELÍAS MIGUEL MUÑOZ

When you slip
slowly and lovingly
through my fingers
I cannot hold you
and explain a thousand things
Each time you smile
and show me your shoes with buckles
or tell me a story
of space flights
(How you would love to be a princess
in those absurd and bloody wars)
Each time you intrigue* me
with your riddles
with your words
that will always be foreign
to our experience

It isn't a reproach*
sister
Little sister born in this land
It's just that you will never know
of hens nesting

---

* These terms are defined in the glossary.

(Is there anywhere in your childhood
a similar feeling?)
Once upon a time
there was a boy
on paving stones so white
and excursions on foot
toys made of tin
There was also mystery
in the ravines
There were evil pirates
and brave corsairs*

There were lessons
for carving men
out of stone
There was caramel candy
and sweet potato pudding

It isn't a reproach
sister
Little sister born in this land
It's just that you have only
the joy of Disney heroes
Because you will smile
when the ingenious* man
behind the cartoons
makes of you
of every child
a little clown
plastic and ridiculous

---

* These terms are defined in the glossary.

When you slip away
slowly and lovingly
I cannot invent
another childhood for you
cannot offer you mine
also nourished by heroes
but tasting of palm leaf
and *mamoncillo*[1]
It did not suffer the mockery
of expensive toys
that the deceptive
ghost of December
brings to you

When you slip away
slowly and lovingly
we cannot bury together
in the backyard
(That warm and always
open earth)
the models
that will take hold of you
that already stalk you
from their cardboard boxes
and their printed letters
on a glass of milk
or Coca-Cola

It isn't a reproach
sister
Little sister born in this land

_____

1. *mamoncillo* (mah-mohn-SEE-yoh) *n.* honey berry

Elena

PAT MORA

$\mathbf{M}$y Spanish isn't enough.
I remember how I'd smile
listening to my little ones,
understanding every word they'd say,
their jokes, their songs, their plots.
    Vamos a pedirle dulces a mamá.[1] *Vamos.*[2]
But that was in Mexico.
Now my children go to American high schools.
They speak English. At night they sit around
the kitchen table, laugh with one another.
I stand by the stove and feel dumb, alone.
I bought a book to learn English.
My husband frowned, drank more beer.
My oldest said, "*Mamá,* he doesn't want you
to be smarter than he is." I'm forty,
embarrassed at mispronouncing words,
embarrassed at the laughter of my children,
the grocer, the mailman. Sometimes I take
my English book and lock myself in the bathroom,
say the thick words softly,
for if I stop trying, I will be deaf
when my children need my help.

---

1. *Vamos a pedirle dulces a mamá.* (VAH-mohs ah peh-DEER-leh DOOL-sehs ah mah-MAH) Let's go ask Mama for some candy.
2. *Vamos.* (VAH-mohs) *v.* Let's go.

Frutas[1]

RICARDO PAU-LLOSA

Growing up in Miami any tropical fruit I ate
could only be a bad copy of the Real Fruit of Cuba.
Exile meant having to consume false food,
and knowing it in advance. With joy
my parents and grandmother would encounter
Florida-grown *mameyes*[2] and *caimitos*[3] at the market.

---

1. *Frutas* (FROO-tahs) *n. pl.* fruit

2. *mameyes* (mah-MAY-yes) *n. pl.* sweet, tropical fruit

3. *caimitos* (kahee-MEE-tohs) *n. pl.* sweet, tropical fruit; star apple

At home they would take them out of the American bag
and describe the taste that I and my older sister
would, in a few seconds, be privileged to experience
for the first time. We all sat around the table
to welcome into our lives this football-shaped,
brown fruit with the salmon-colored flesh
encircling an ebony* seed. *"Mamey,"*
my grandmother would say with a confirming nod,
as if repatriating* a lost and ruined name.
Then she bent over the plate,
slipped a large slice of *mamey* into her mouth,
then straightened in her chair and, eyes shut,
lost herself in comparison and memory.
I waited for her face to return with a judgment.
"No, not even the shadow of the ones back home."
She kept eating, more calmly,
and I began tasting the sweet and creamy pulp
trying to raise the volume of its flavor
so that it might become a Cuban *mamey.* "The good
Cuban *mameyes* didn't have *primaveras*,"[4] she said
after the second large gulp, knocking her spoon
against a lump in the fruit and winking.
So at once I erased the lumps in my mental mamey.
I asked her how the word for "spring"
came to signify "lump" in a *mamey.* She shrugged.
"Next you'll want to know how we lost a country."

---

4. *primaveras* (pree-mah-VEH-rahs) *n. pl.* literally meaning "springtime," used here to mean "lumps"

*These terms are defined in the glossary.

Home

GUSTAVO PÉREZ FIRMAT

Give a guy a break.
Take him back, let him step
on soil that's his or feels his,
let him have a tongue,
a story, a geography.
Let him not trip back and forth between
bilingualisms,
hyphens,
explanations.
As it is he's a walking-talking bicameral* page.
Two hemispheres and neither one likes the other.
Ambidextrous.*
Omnipossibilist.*
Multivocal.*
Let him stop having to translate himself
to himself
endlessly.
Give the guy a break:
crease him, slip him into an envelope,
address it, and let him go.
Home.

---

* These terms are defined in the glossary.

Which Line Is This?
I Forget[1]

LORNA DEE CERVANTES

What a fool's game I'm playing,
this foolish game called
"Shame."
Where the rules are rigid
and the stakes are high
and you play for keeps.
Constantly running,
lying,
making up lies to cover my lies,
pretending,
hiding from something I know nothing about.
Talking fast
because I'm not quite sure of what I'm saying.
Feeling close kin to the Ugly Duckling.
Not a turkey
yet
not quite a swan.
Pretending I'm "White"
when they tell me I'm "Mexican."
Pretending I'm "Mexican"
when they tell me I'm "White."

"Hey, Boss Man!"
Wherever you are
in Heaven
or in Hell
I'm not fussy.
I just want someone to tell me which line this is
                        I forget

---

1. Lorna Dee Cervantes wrote this poem in 1969 at age 15.

Returning

ELÍAS MIGUEL MUÑOZ

While in the barrio[1] no one spoke
of leaving or of telegrams
And we all dreamed about apples
and mint-flavored chewing gum.
Remember?

---

1. barrio (BAHR-ee-oh) *n.* neighborhood

The rice and black beans
no longer satisfied us.
Without the eternal summer,
without dirt streets and sugar cane
we would no longer have dark skin.
The lines would end,
and so would the *quimbumbia*,[2]
the *yuca*,[3]
and the mud puddles.

So we could sing, later,
to a different beat.
So we could forget your
conga[4] player's outfit.
So we could chew away
until we had no teeth.
So we could speak of the things
we lost,
things we never had.
So that later,
under the northern skies,
we could begin to dream
about returning.

---

2. *quimbumbia* (keem-BOOM-byah) *n.* a plant that grows in the Caribbean
   area
3. *yuca* (YOO-kuh) *n.* an edible root used in Latin American cooking
4. **conga** (KAHNG-guh) *adj.* a type of drum

FAMILIAR LANDSCAPES: PLACES CALLED HOME

Los New Yorks

VICTOR HERNÁNDEZ CRUZ

In the news that sails through the air
Like the shaking seeds of maracas[1]
I find you out

Suena[2]

You don't have to move here
Just stand on the corner
Everything will pass you by
Like a merry-go-round the red
bricks will swing past your eyes
They will melt
So   old
will move out by themselves

Suena

I present you the tall skyscrapers
as merely huge palm trees with lights

Suena

The roaring of the trains is a fast
guaguanco[3]
dance of the ages

---

1. **maracas** (mah-RAH-kahs) *n. pl.* gourd-shaped rattles containing loose pebbles, shaken to beat out a rhythm
2. **suena** (SWEH-nah) *v.* it sounds
3. **guaguanco** (gwah-GWAHN-koh) *n.* a popular dance

Suena

Snow falls
Coconut chips galore
Take the train to Caguas[4]
and the bus is only ten cents
to Aguas Buenas[5]

Suena

A tropical wave settled here
And it is pulling the sun
with a romp
No one knows what to do

Suena

I am going home now
I am settled there with my fruits
Everything tastes good today
Even the ones that are grown here
Taste like they're from outer space
Walk y Suena
Do it strange
Los New Yorks.

---

4. Caguas (KAH-gwahs) a town in Puerto Rico
5. Aguas Buenas (AH-gwahs BWEH-nahs) a town in Puerto Rico

Los Angeles

BEN LUNA

A bit of sprawling madness
A bush-land Babylon*
A den of thieves . . . once?
                    Still.

The summer nights
            Are pleasant there
On Hammel Street
            Where I was born.
The people dream in Spanish
And live as best they can.

---

* This term is defined in the glossary.

Tony Went to the Bodega[1] but He Didn't Buy Anything

for Angel Guadalupe

MARTÍN ESPADA

Tony's father left the family
and the Long Island* city projects,
leaving a mongrel-skinny puertorriqueño[2] boy
nine years old
who had to find work.

Makengo the Cuban
let him work at the bodega.
In grocery aisles
he learned the steps of the dry-mop mambo,[3]
banging the cash register
like piano percussion
in the spotlight of Machito's orchestra,
polite with the abuelas[4] who bought on credit,
practicing the grin on customers
he'd seen Makengo grin
with his bad yellow teeth.

---

1. **Bodega** (boh-DEH-gah) *n.* a grocery store
2. **puertorriqueño** (pwer-toh-rree-KEH-nyoh) *adj.* Puerto Rican
3. **mambo** (MAHM-boh) *n.* a popular Latin American dance
4. **abuelas** (ah-BWEH-lahs) *n. pl.* grandmothers

* This term is defined in the glossary.

Tony left the projects too,
with a scholarship for law school.
But he cursed the cold primavera[5]
in Boston;
the cooking of his neighbors
left no smell in the hallway,
and no one spoke Spanish
(not even the radio).

So Tony walked without a map
through the city,
a landscape of hostile condominiums
and the darkness of white faces,
sidewalk-searcher lost
till he discovered the projects.

Tony went to the bodega
but he didn't buy anything:
he sat by the doorway satisfied
to watch la gente[6] (people
island-brown as him)
crowd in and out,
hablando español,[7]
thought: this is beautiful,
and grinned
his bodega grin.

This is a rice and beans
success story:
today Tony lives on Tremont Street,
above the bodega.

---

5. primavera (pree-mah-VEH-rah) *n.* spring

6. la gente (lah HEN-teh) *n.* the people

7. hablando español (ah-BLAHN-doh es-pah-NYOHL) speaking Spanish

Field Poem

GARY SOTO

When the foreman whistled
My brother and I
Shouldered our hoes,
Leaving the field.
We returned to the bus
Speaking
In broken English, in broken Spanish
The restaurant food,
The tickets to a dance
We wouldn't buy with our pay.

From the smashed bus window,
I saw the leaves of cotton plants
Like small hands
Waving good-bye.

Lesson 1

PAT MORA

The desert is powerless
when thunder shakes the hot air
and unfamiliar raindrops slide
on rocks, sand, *mesquite*,[1]
when unfamiliar raindrops overwhelm
her, distort her face.
But after the storm, she breathes deeply,
caressed by a fresh sweet calm.
My Mother smiles rainbows.

When I feel shaken, powerless
to stop my bruising sadness,
I hear My Mother whisper:

Mi'ja[2]

don't fear your hot tears
cry away the storm, then listen, listen.

---

1. *mesquite* (mehs-KEET) *n.* a plant that grows in the desert
2. *Mi'ja* (MEE-hah) *n.* contraction of *Mi hija* (mee EE-hah), which means "my daughter"

Lesson 2

PAT MORA

Small, white fairies dance
on the *Rio Grande*.[1] Usually they swim
Deep through their days and nights
hiding from our eyes, but when the white
sun pulls them up, up
they leap about, tiny shimmering stars.

The desert says: feel the sun
luring you from your dark, sad waters,
burst through the surface

dance

---

1. *Rio Grande* (REE-oh GRAND) the river that runs along the border
between Mexico and the United States

Pueblo[1] *Winter*

BERNICE ZAMORA

Sparrows in Pueblo perch on empty
elm branches cocking their heads
at each other or at each shadow
under the warming winter sun.

They watch each other watch
each other and seem, at times,
more passive than their shadows
under the warming winter sun

until a robin flights by to break
their bobbing trance. Another robin
joins the first. Both alight
on a chokeberry bush

scattering the flapping
sparrows to the pole lines above.
From the lines they watch
the robins on the cherry bush.

One robin pecks at a drying cherry
while the silent other lays witness
to the act; so, too, the sparrows
under the warming sun.

---

1. *Pueblo* (PWEHB-loh) a city in southern Colorado

THE FAMILY: HONORING LOVED ONES

Matriarch*

FRANCISCO X. ALARCÓN

my dark
grandmother

would brush
her long hair

seated out
on her patio

even ferns
would bow

to her splendor
and her power

---

* This term is defined in the glossary.

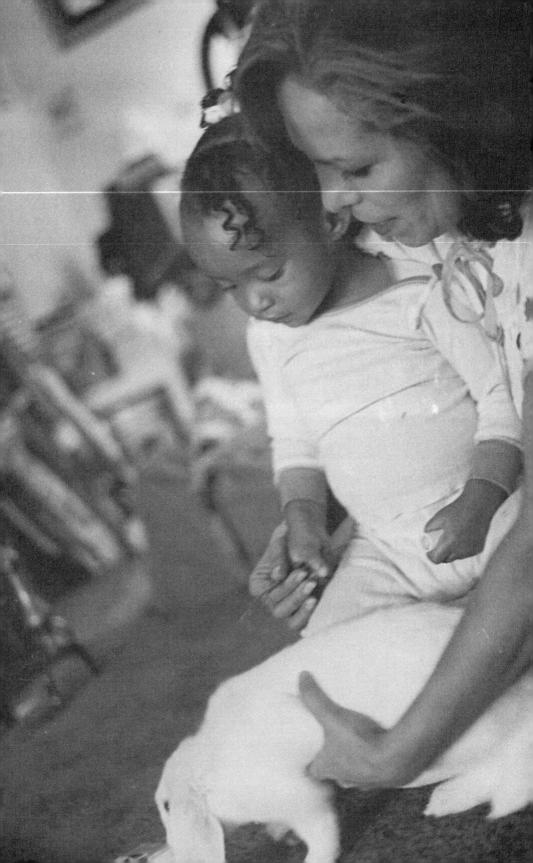

Mamacita[1]

JUDITH ORTIZ COFER

Mamacita hummed all day long
over the caboose* kitchen
of our railroad flat.*
From my room I'd hear her *humm,*
crossing her path, I'd catch her *umm.*
No words slowed the flow
of Mamacita's soulful sounds;
it was *humm* over the yellow rice,
and *umm* over the black beans.
Up and down two syllables she'd climb
and slide—each note a task accomplished.
From chore to chore, she was the prima donna*
in her daily operetta.*
Mamacita's wordless song was her connection
to the oversoul,
her link with life,
her mantra,*
a lifeline to her own Laughing Buddha,*
as she dragged her broom
across a lifetime of linoleum floors.

---

1. *Mamacita* (mah-mah-SEE-tah) *n.* an affectionate term for "mother"
* These terms are defined in the glossary.

My Father in the Navy: A Childhood Memory

JUDITH ORTIZ COFER

Stiff and immaculate
in the white cloth of his uniform
and a round cap on his head like a halo,
he was an apparition* on leave from a shadow-world
and only flesh and blood when he rose from below
the waterline where he kept watch over the engines
and dials making sure the ship parted the waters
on a straight course.
Mother, brother and I kept vigil*
on the nights and dawns of his arrivals,
watching the corner beyond the neon sign of a quasar*
for the flash of white our father like an angel
heralding a new day.
His homecomings were the verses
we composed over the years making up
the siren's* song that kept him coming back
from the bellies of iron whales
and into our nights
like the evening prayer.

---

* These terms are defined in the glossary.

Sweet Drama

LUIS OMAR SALINAS

On a night like this . . .
with rain in the distant mountains
soup steaming in the kitchen
my father reads the newspaper
polite, gentle, and at peace
with himself nearing his 80th birthday
There is little in the news
that disturbs him now.
He is happy God has
given him a long life
a woman to love and a son
who knows enough
to walk outside and praise
the olive groves and figs
to whistle along with the sunlight
as they both saunter along
the quiet farming roads . . .

My mother sleeps the sleep of angels
the blue sleep of gardenias touched
by moonlight. Today
she poured orange juice
on her cereal by mistake
she smiled and shook her head—
old age here has the makings
of a sweet drama . . .

My Mother Pieced Quilts

TERESA PALOMO ACOSTA

they were just meant as covers
in winters
as weapons
against pounding january winds

but it was just that every morning I awoke to these
october ripened canvases
passed my hand across their cloth faces
and began to wonder how you pieced
all these together
these strips of gentle communion cotton and flannel
    nightgowns
wedding organdies
dime store velvets

how you shaped patterns square and oblong* and round
positioned
balanced
then cemented them
with your thread
a steel needle
a thimble

---

* This term is defined in the glossary.

how the thread darted in and out
galloping along the frayed* edges, tucking them in
as you did us at night
oh how you stretched and turned and re-arranged
your michigan spring faded curtain pieces
my father's santa fe[1] work shirt
the summer denims, the tweeds of fall

in the evening you sat at your canvas
—our cracked linoleum floor the drawing board
me lounging on your arm
and you staking out the plan:
whether to put the lilac purple of easter against the
    red plaid of winter-going-
into-spring

whether to mix a yellow with blue and white and paint the
corpus christi* noon when my father held your hand
whether to shape a five-point star from the
somber black silk you wore to grandmother's funeral

you were the river current
carrying the roaring notes
forming them into pictures of a little boy reclining
a swallow flying
you were the caravan* master at the reins
driving your threaded needle artillery across the mosaic*
    cloth bridges
delivering yourself in separate testimonies*

---

1. **Santa Fe** (SAN-tuh FAY) capital of New Mexico
* These terms are defined in the glossary.

oh mother you plunged me sobbing and laughing
into our past
into the river crossing at five
into the spinach fields
into the plainview cotton rows
into tuberculosis wards
into braids and muslin dresses
sewn hard and taut to withstand the thrashings of
   twenty-five years

stretched out they lay
armed/ready/shouting/celebrating

knotted with love
the quilts sing on

Father's Day On Longwood Avenue

for Charlie

SANDRA MARÍA ESTEVES

Returning to that abandoned past of youth,
Bronx* neighborhood of her father's house.
A five story structure, still, but standing.
Where once his tall husky frame sat
in a top floor window, drinking beer.
As she watched from below,
in awe of this person, she barely knew.

Three blocks south from him
the Beck Street tenement she first claimed home,
last year, torn to the ground.
Nineteen years tumbled into shadows,
dust traces of rubble remain,
names of neighbors, best friends, disappeared.

---

* This term is defined in the glossary.

And in the place where her room once held her,
where she became alive, cried,
and learned to love her mother,
studying world through windows facing sun,
chanting incantations* to the Moon
of top forty hit parades
in fourth floor ghetto repertoire.*
Space of broken concrete, limping paint,
so dear, the only water she knew,
now a lane through a park where lovers walk
over new matted rugs of prefabricated* astroturf.
While memories of building linger in trees,
Titi[1] Julia's apartment one, where life began,
now air and space where birds fly in symbolic liberation
of land reclaimed by wind,
spirit of her home set free,
an unraveled karma.*

While the shell of her father's house endures,
a monument braced against the elements.
Roof leaking to basement, only rats take notice.
Winds howling lonely sonatas,* no one hears.

A single pigeon flies west, silhouetting sunset.
She remembers a young woman of thirteen
looking for the last time
at this stranger not seen for twenty-six years,
wondering
who he was.

---

1. **Titi** (TEE-tee) *n.* an affectionate term for "aunt"

* These terms are defined in the glossary.

Ironing Their Clothes

JULIA ALVAREZ

With a hot glide up, then down, his shirts,
I ironed out my father's back, cramped
and worried with work. I stroked the yoke,
and breast pocket, collar and cuffs,
until the rumpled heap relaxed into the shape
of my father's broad chest, the shoulders shrugged off
the world, the collapsed arms spread for a hug.
And if there'd been a face above the buttondown neck,
I would have pressed the forehead out, I would
have made a boy again out of that tired man!

If I clung to her skirt as she sorted the wash
or put out a line, my mother frowned,
a crease down each side of her mouth.
This is no time for love! But here
I could linger over her wrinkled bedjacket,
kiss at the damp puckers of her wrists
with the hot tip. Here I caressed complications
of darts, scallops, ties, pleats which made
her outfits test of the patience of my passion.
Here I could lay my dreaming iron on her lap.

The smell of baked cotton rose from the board
and blew with a breeze out the window
to a family wardrobe drying on the clothesline,
all needing a touch of my iron. Here I could tickle
the underarms of my big sister's petticoat
or secretly pat the backside of her pyjamas.
For she too would have warned me not to muss
her fresh blouses, starched jumpers, and smocks,
all that my careful hand had ironed out,
forced to express my excess love on cloth.

Dear Tía[1]

CAROLINA HOSPITAL

I do not write.
The years have frightened me away.
My life in a land so familiarly foreign,
a denial of your presence.
Your name is mine.
One black and white photograph of your youth,
all I hold on to.
One story of your past.

The pain comes not from nostalgia.*
I do not miss your voice urging me in play,
your smiles,
or your pride when others called you my mother.
I cannot close my eyes and feel your soft skin;
listen to your laughter;
smell the sweetness of your bath.
I write because I cannot remember at all.

---

1. Tía (TEE-ah) *n.* aunt

* This term is defined in the glossary.

In a Neighborhood in Los Angeles

FRANCISCO X. ALARCÓN

I learned
Spanish
from my grandma

mijito[1]
don't cry
she'd tell me

on the mornings
my parents
would leave

to work
at the fish
canneries

my grandma
would chat
with chairs

sing them
old
songs

dance
waltzes with them
in the kitchen

---

1. *mijito* (mee-HEE-toh) *n.* contraction of *mi hijo* (mee EE-hoh), which
means "my son"

when she'd say
niño barrigón[2]
she'd laugh

with my grandma
I learned
to count clouds

to point out
in flowerpots
mint leaves

my grandma
wore moons
on her dress

Mexico's mountains
deserts
ocean

in her eyes
I'd see them
in her braids

I'd touch them
in her voice
smell them

one day
I was told:
she went far away

but still
I feel her
with me

whispering
in my ear
mijito

---

2. ***niño barrigón*** (NEE-nyoh bah-rree-GOHN) affectionate term for a chubby
   child

INSIGHTS: UNDERSTANDING OURSELVES, APPRECIATING OTHERS

Religious Instructions For Young Casualties

SANDRA MARÍA ESTEVES

Believe in yourself.
Be all that you can.
Look for your fate among the stars.
Imagine you are your best when being yourself
the best way you can.

Believe in yourself. Be all you want to be.
Open your mind, a window to the world,
different ways of thinking, seeing,
but be yourself—it's the best.

Become your dreams, visions to live by.
No matter what anyone says,
believe you can do it.
Day by day, a little at a time.
Be patient.

Believe you can find a way
to assemble the puzzle called life,
forming pictures that make some kind of sense.
Even when pieces fall scattered to the ground,
disappearing into the finite* void,*
forever lost, never to be found,
choosing your future from those that are left,
like one piece from some other dimension.

---

*These terms are defined in the glossary.

Maybe a corner triangle shape of sky,
or zigzag of ocean floor with seaweed and one school of
fish,
or maybe a centerpiece on the table in some fancy dining
    room,
or patch of window lace curtain next to flowered bouquet,
wind blowing through sunlight, which some artist will
    paint someday.
Or bouncing feet on the moon,
walking in giant moon leaps, talking moon talk,
deep into research in your flying laboratory.

Be all that you can, but believe in yourself.
Climb the stairway of your imagination, one step after
    another.
Growing like the leaf, blossoming into a great tree,
complete with squirrels, nests, universe all around.

Be all that you can,
just believe in yourself.

Mestizo[1]

FRANCISCO X. ALARCÓN

my name
is not
Francisco

there is
an Arab
within me

who prays
three times
each day

behind
my Roman
nose

there is
a Phoenician*
smiling

my eyes
still see
Sevilla[2]

---

1. *Mestizo* (mes-TEE-soh) *n.* a person of mixed background, usually of
   Spanish and Indian heritages
2. **Sevilla** (seh-VEE-yah) a city in southern Spain

* This term is defined in the glossary.

but
my mouth
is Olmec*

my dark
hands are
Toltec*

my cheekbones
fierce
Chichimec*

my feet
recognize
no border

no rule
no code
no lord

for this
wanderer's
heart

_____

* These terms are defined in the glossary.

The Beauty of Me and My People[1]

LORNA DEE CERVANTES

Funny how I never noticed it before
but there's a beauty in my smooth amber skin
in the rich ginger-chocolate perfection.
It was foolish to think that pale
white, veined skin
was beauty.
My hair is also a wonder—raven black
sexy—against the whiteness of a pillow.
Thick and strong
deep and dark
                              shiny . . .
And my dark Spanish/Indian eyes
glossy and clear
a deep mahogany brown,
in dim light they blend in darkness . . .
And the dark of my eyes
And the dark of my hair
against the amber background of my skin
                    paint a very pretty picture.

---

1. Lorna Dee Cervantes wrote this poem in 1969 at age 14.

I'm a Chicana[1]
from Thoughts of a Chicana Woman

RITA MENDOZA

You could pass for an Angelo, they tell me if you tried
I said "I'm a Chicana," my head bent-down—I cried.
You could pass for a French girl, they tell me if you tried
I said "I'm a Chicana," eyes downcast—tried to hide.
You could pass for a Spanish, they tell me if you tried.
I said "I'm a Chicana," eyes straight-ahead, sad, dried.
You could pass for a Chicana, no one has ever tried
I said "Thank you," my head held up with pride.

---

1. **Chicana** (chee-KAH-nah) *adj.* a woman or girl of Mexican background, born in the United States

Side 32

VICTOR HERNÁNDEZ CRUZ

I am glad that I am not one of those
Big Con Edison* pipes that sits by the
River crying smoke
I am glad that I am not the doorknob
Of a police car patrolling the Lower
East Side
How cool I am not a subway token
That has been lost and is sitting
Quietly and lonely by the edge of
A building on 47th Street
I am nothing and no one
I am the possibility of everything
I am a man in this crazy city
I am a door and a glass of water
I am a guitar string cutting through the
Smog
Vibrating and bringing morning
My head is a butterfly
Over the traffic jams

---

* This term is defined in the glossary.

[I'm Sitting in My History Class]

RICHARD OLIVAS

I'm sitting in my history class,
The instructor commences* rapping,
I'm in my U.S. History class,
And I'm on the verge of napping.

The Mayflower landed on Plymouth Rock.
Tell me more! Tell me more!
Thirteen colonies were settled.
I've heard it all before.

What did he say?
Dare I ask him to reiterate?*
Oh why bother
It sounded like he said,
George Washington's my father.

I'm reluctant to believe it,
I suddenly raise my mano.[1]
If George Washington's my father,
Why wasn't he Chicano?[2]

---

1. **mano** (MAH-noh) *n.* hand
2. **Chicano** (chee-KAH-noh) *adj.* a man or boy of Mexican background, born in the United States

* These terms are defined in the glossary.

Little Has Been Written About Cowards

ELÍAS MIGUEL MUÑOZ

Little has been written about cowards
That's what a friend told me once
because I didn't dare to dive
You must do it
he said
because little has been written about cowards

And I dove
And when I came up by a natural impulse
as though some powerful hand
made of water and salt
pushed and pulled me
                    from what could be
                              the end

I thought that perhaps my friend was right
that little has been written about those people

And thinking about it
it also occurred to me
that maybe the cowards would describe my leap
and they would speak of my challenged masculinity*
of the tests I will endure
to prove my valor*
that maybe the cowards
would laughingly watch me
dry and free
from the bow
that maybe the cowards
could fill up in their own way
the emptiness they leave in the world
the justification* of the cowards
about whom
according to my good friend
little has been written

_____

* These terms are defined in the glossary.

Mi Padre[1]

MARIO GARZA

I saw my father
  the other morning
I saw his eyes
  no tan negros
   pero con la
    misma mirada[2]

He looked different
  más joven,[3] the way
I remember him
  as a child
It was the same hair
  and the same moustache
But I could not see
  his diente de oro[4]
   when he smiled
    at me this time

---

1. *Mi Padre* (mee PAH-dreh) my father
2. **no tan negros pero con la misma mirada** (noh tahn NEH-grohs PEH-roh kohn lah MEES-mah mee-RAH-dah) not as black, but with the same expression
3. **más joven** (mahs HOH-ven) younger
4. **diente de oro** (DYEN-teh theh OH-roh) gold tooth

Without thinking
   I reached for him
      quería abrazarlo
         otra vez[5]
Then I realized
   I was reaching
      at the image
      reflected in
        my mirror.

---

5. quería abrazarlo otra vez (keh-REE-ah ah-brah-SAHR-loh OH-trah ves) I
wanted to embrace him again.

Things of Our Childhood

to Marc, in his twenty-first year

ALMA LUZ VILLANUEVA

I watch you defy your death,
climbing the sheer mountain cliff
until you become a dot.
I do not say, "Come back,
you'll kill yourself!" No, I stopped
that a while ago, and I watch you
climb with joy, as I climb with joy;

so I understand, only you go straight up
and I go sideways, then up—but I get
there. We talk and the lake listens,
then the fire, and finally, just the
stars. The first night we sat on granite
as galaxies appeared in the dark, cold
lake; I told you things of my childhood,
and, later, things of your childhood.
I lead, you lead. Mother, son.
Man and woman. Backpacking out,

you go ahead; I stop often, touching
trees, stones, whispering my goodbyes,
knowing there are no goodbyes. Knowing
you will greet me. Soon.

THE POEM
IN
REVIEW

SEEKING A NEW LIFE: CONFLICTS AND CHALLENGES

Immigrants (p. 2)

1. How does this poem remind you of your own feelings about wanting to be liked by others?
2. How do you think Mora views immigrants who give up their cultural heritage for new beliefs and values?
3. Briefly discuss the poet's message.

A New Refugee (p. 3)

1. How does this poem reflect the way you feel about strangers?
2. What do the words *countryman* and *stranger* in the last stanza suggest about the way Veiga feels toward other Cuban immigrants?
3. What does the line "In this house we are not without a gun" reveal about the poem's theme?

People of the Harvest (p. 4)

1. How did reading this poem help you understand the lives of fieldworkers?
2. What does this poem reveal about Quiñónez's feelings for her people?
3. How does this poem reflect the unit theme of conflicts and challenges that immigrants experience in this country?

The Maestro's Barber Shop (p. 6)

1. Describe a special place in your neighborhood that this poem calls to mind.
2. How do you think Vásquez feels about the maestro and his customers?
3. Discuss how the last five lines of the poem reflect the unit theme of seeking a new life in the United States.

Mestizo (p. 8)

1. How does this poem make you feel? Which words, phrases, or images help to stir these emotions?
2. What does this poem reveal about Salinas's attitude toward the conditions his people endure in the United States?
3. Which conflicts and challenges does Salinas present in this poem? How do they relate to the unit theme?

In a Farmhouse (p. 10)

1. How would you feel if you were in the place of the farmworker in the poem?
2. What impression of farmworkers does Salinas convey in the poem?
3. What is the central message of the poem?

Working Hands (p. 11)

1. After reading this poem, what do you think about the experiences of ethnic groups in this country?
2. What does Alarcón reveal about his feelings toward his people?
3. What is the main idea of this poem?

On heroes *(p. 12)*

1. Who are some of your heroes? Why do you admire these people?
2. According to Padilla, what role do heroes play in society?
3. How does the last line of this poem relate to the unit theme of seeking a new life?

UNIT TWO

REFLECTIONS: REMEMBERING PEOPLE AND PLACES

My Mother's Homeland *(p. 15)*

1. How is the idea of a homeland in this poem similar to or different from your own?
2. What does this poem reveal about Malé's attitude toward her mother's homeland?
3. What do you think is the theme of this poem?

We Live by What We See at Night *(p. 16)*

1. How does this poem make you feel? Which specific words or phrases evoke those feelings?
2. What does Espada reveal about his feelings for Puerto Rico, his father's homeland?
3. What is the central idea of this poem?

La Casa   (p. 18)

1. What feelings about your home does this poem awaken in you?
2. How do Catacalos's feelings about the house reflect her feelings about her cultural heritage?
3. How does this poem relate to the unit theme of remembering people and places?

Granizo   (p. 19)

1. What season or type of weather do you usually associate with your home? Why?
2. Why does the hail remind Quintana of his grandfather?
3. What do you think is the theme of this poem?

The Latin Deli   (p. 20)

1. Briefly describe the foods you associate with your cultural heritage.
2. In this poem, how does Cofer show the importance of preserving cultural traditions?
3. How does this poem relate to the unit theme of remembering people and places?

Coffee Bloom   (p. 22)

1. What is your favorite line or image in this poem? Why?
2. How are the roots of the coffee bush similar to Morales's cultural roots?
3. How does the central message of this poem reflect the unit theme?

jíbaro *(p. 23)*

1. How does this poem affect the way you think about the work of farmers?
2. Which specific words or phrases in the poem reveal Laviera's attitude toward the *jíbaros* of his homeland?
3. What is the central message of this poem?

December's Picture *(p. 24)*

1. What smells, sounds, or visual images do you associate with the house of a special relative or friend?
2. What do you think this poem reveals about Pigño's attitude toward her cultural heritage?
3. How does this poem relate to the unit theme of reflecting on the past?

My Grandmother Would Rock Quietly and Hum *(p. 26)*

1. Which traditions from your culture have you learned from a grandparent or another special person?
2. What does the seventh stanza of the poem suggest about Adamé's feelings for his grandmother?
3. What is the main idea of this poem?

UNIT THREE

IDENTITY: BALANCING TWO CULTURES

Applying for a Civil Service Job (p. 30)

1. What questions do you have after reading this poem?
2. What do you think is Garza's point of view in this poem? How does the repeated use of the question "Why not?" reflect this point of view?
3. How does the poem's theme relate to the theme of identity?

The Space Between (p. 32)

1. What is your favorite line or image in the poem? Why?
2. How do you think Ortiz de Montellano feels about her Latina identity? How does the title of the poem support your answer?
3. The author states that she chooses "to live in the middle of the stream." How does this statement help you connect the poem to the unit theme of balancing two cultures?

Nochebuena (p. 34)

1. How does the last stanza of the poem make you feel?
2. What does this poem reveal about Caicedo's attitude toward her cultural identity?
3. What do you think is the central message of this poem?

piñones   *(p. 36)*

1. What thoughts do you have about your family traditions after reading this poem?
2. How does Quintana's family preserve its Mexican heritage?
3. What is the central idea of this poem?

Side 12   *(p. 36)*

1. What thoughts or questions do you have after reading this poem?
2. In this short poem, how does Cruz reveal his feelings about his cultural heritage?
3. Briefly discuss how this poem is related to the unit theme.

Here   *(p. 37)*

1. What was your reaction to this poem?
2. What does Esteves suggest can happen when people try to balance two cultures?
3. What do you believe is the poet's message?

Little Sister Born in This Land   *(p. 38)*

1. How do the ideas expressed in this poem relate to an experience in your own life?
2. In this poem, Muñoz reveals the differences between children raised in the United States and those raised in his homeland. What do you think is his attitude toward those differences?
3. What is the theme of this poem?

Elena   *(p. 41)*

1. How did reading this poem help you understand the language problems many immigrants experience in the United States?
2. According to Mora, why is it important for a mother to speak the same language as her children?
3. Briefly discuss the message of the poem.

Frutas   *(p. 42)*

1. Which foods from your cultural heritage does this poem call to mind?
2. How do you think Pau-Llosa views the differences between his Cuban heritage and his U.S. values?
3. How does this poem reflect the unit theme of balancing two cultures?

Home   *(p. 44)*

1. What emotions does this poem awaken in you?
2. What does this poem reveal about Firmat's attitude toward his cultural identity?
3. How does the title of this poem reveal the theme?

Which Line Is This? I Forget   *(p. 45)*

1. Cervantes wrote this poem as a teenager. Why do you think teenagers sometimes feel ashamed of who they are?
2. How do the lines "Not a turkey/yet/not quite a swan" reflect Cervantes's attitude toward her cultural identity?
3. How do the last four lines of the first stanza help you connect this poem to the unit theme?

Returning

(p. 46)

1. Have you ever dreamed of returning to a place where you lived or visited? Explain.
2. In this poem, what does Muñoz tell you about the dreams and the realities of living in a new country?
3. How does the theme of this poem relate to the unit theme of identity?

UNIT FOUR

FAMILIAR LANDSCAPES: PLACES CALLED HOME

Los New Yorks

(p. 49)

1. How does this poem influence the way that you view New York City?
2. Why do you think Cruz connects the landscape of New York to the landscape of Puerto Rico?
3. How do the last two lines reveal the central idea of this poem?

Los Angeles

(p. 51)

1. How does this poem make you feel about life in Los Angeles?
2. What does the poem reveal about Luna's attitude toward Los Angeles?
3. What is the theme of this poem?

Tony Went to the Bodega but He Didn't Buy Anything

(p. 52)

1. How does this poem affect how you feel about your own neighborhood or community?

2. What does the poem reveal about Espada's attitude toward his people?
3. What do you think is the central message of this poem?

Field Poem (p. 54)

1. What thoughts did you have after reading this poem?
2. What does the poem suggest about Soto's attitude toward being a fieldworker?
3. How does the title of this poem reflect the theme?

Lesson 1 (p. 56)

1. Describe the images that you usually associate with a desert landscape.
2. Mora refers to the desert as "My Mother." What does this reveal about her feelings for the desert?
3. Briefly discuss the message of this poem.

Lesson 2 (p. 57)

1. How does this poem change the way you think about the desert?
2. How does the poem reveal Mora's creative imagination?
3. In one sentence, state the poet's message.

Pueblo Winter (p. 58)

1. What feelings or memories about nature does this poem awaken in you?
2. How are Zamora's feelings about nature reflected in this poem?
3. How does the poem relate to the unit theme?

THE FAMILY: HONORING LOVED ONES

Matriarch (p. 60)

1. What qualities do you usually associate with grandparents? Why?
2. Which of his grandmother's qualities do you think Alarcón admires? Which lines from the poem support your answer?
3. What is the theme of this poem?

Mamacita (p. 62)

1. In what ways does "Mamacita" remind you of a special person in your life?
2. What do you think Cofer learns about life from watching her mother work?
3. How does Cofer honor her mother by writing this poem?

My Father in the Navy: A Childhood Memory (p. 63)

1. What childhood memories of your own does this poem bring to mind?
2. What does this poem reveal about the way Cofer views her father?
3. What is the central idea of this poem?

Sweet Drama (p. 64)

1. How does this poem change the way you view older people?
2. What values do you think Salinas learned from his parents? How does the title of the poem reflect these values?
3. Briefly discuss the theme of this poem.

My Mother Pieced Quilts   *(p. 65)*

1. Which traditions in your family does this poem bring to mind?
2. How is Acosta's poem similar to her mother's quilts?
3. What is the poet's message?

Father's Day On Longwood Avenue   *(p. 68)*

1. What questions do you have after reading this poem?
2. What impression of the relationship between the young woman and her father does Esteves convey? Which lines from the poem support your answer?
3. What is the theme of this poem?

Ironing Their Clothes   *(p. 70)*

1. In what ways do you show your appreciation for your family?
2. What does Alvarez reveal in this poem about her feelings toward her family?
3. What is the poet's message?

Dear Tía   *(p. 71)*

1. How does this poem make you feel? Which words, phrases, or images evoke these feelings?
2. What kind of relationship do you think Hospital wanted to have with her aunt? Which lines from the poem support your answer?
3. What is the main idea of this poem?

In a Neighborhood in Los Angeles   *(p. 72)*

1. Does this poem remind you of a special relationship you have with a family member or friend? Explain.
2. Which lines in the poem reveal how Alarcón connects the memory of his grandmother to his Mexican heritage?
3. How does this poem reflect the unit theme of honoring loved ones?

UNIT SIX

INSIGHTS: UNDERSTANDING OURSELVES, APPRECIATING OTHERS

Religious Instructions For Young Casualties (p. 75)

1. How does this poem influence the way you think about your goals and dreams for the future?
2. How does the title relate to the ideas Esteves conveys in the poem?
3. How does the theme of this poem reflect the unit theme of understanding ourselves?

Mestizo (p. 78)

1. What thoughts do you have about your own cultural heritage after reading this poem?
2. How would you describe Alarcón's attitude toward his mixed cultural heritage?
3. What is the central message of the poem?

The Beauty of Me and My People (p. 80)

1. How does this poem affect your ideas about beauty?
2. Which line in the poem suggests that Cervantes's self-image is closely tied to her cultural heritage?
3. What do you believe is the poet's message?

I'm a Chicana (p. 81)

1. How does this poem remind you of an experience in your own life or in the life of someone you know?
2. What does the poem suggest about Mendoza's feelings about herself?
3. How does this poem reflect the unit theme of understanding ourselves?

Side 32 (p. 82)

1. How does this poem make you feel happy about yourself?
2. How would you describe Cruz's feelings about himself? Choose one line from the poem that supports your answer.
3. What is the central idea of this poem?

[I'm Sitting in My History Class] (p. 83)

1. How are you able to relate this poem to experiences in your own life?
2. What questions about himself does Olivas reveal in the poem?
3. How do the last two lines connect the poem to the unit theme?

Little Has Been Written About Cowards (p. 84)

1. How does this poem influence the way you think about bravery and cowardice?
2. What do you think is Muñoz's attitude toward cowards? What does he suggest about the way they are viewed by others?
3. How does this poem reflect the unit theme of appreciating others?

Mi Padre (p. 86)

1. What was your reaction to this poem?
2. How do you think Garza feels about his father? Which lines in the poem support your answer?
3. How does the theme of this poem relate to the unit theme?

Things of Our Childhood (p. 88)

1. What feelings or emotions do you have after reading this poem?
2. What does this poem reveal about Villanueva's understanding of the relationship between mother and child?
3. What is the central idea of this poem?

BIOGRAPHIES OF POETS

Teresa Palomo Acosta (1949–) is a journalist who studied at the University of Texas and Columbia University. As a child growing up in Texas, Acosta enjoyed the stories her grandfather told of his boyhood in Mexico and his life as a cowboy. These stories sparked Acosta's interest in literature. The poem "My Mother Pieced Quilts," which appears in this volume, was written in an hour as an assignment for a college class. The poem was read at the University of Southern California in 1973 during the first national festival of Chicano literature.

Leonard Adamé (1947–) was born in California's San Joaquin Valley. Among his childhood memories are summers spent on his uncle's farm and the delicious tortillas his grandmother made for him. After an undistinguished high school career, Adamé played in clubs and toured the country as a rock musician. His poetry is personal and reflects a tenderness and an intensity of feeling. Adamé's book *Cantos pa'la memoria*, published in 1979, contains poems devoted to members of his family. His poems have also been published in anthologies and in the *American Poetry Review*. Adamé has taught at California State University.

Francisco X. Alarcón was born in Los Angeles but grew up in Mexico. His volumes of poetry include *The Earthquake Poems*, *Tattoos*, *Body in Flames/Cuerpo en Llamas*, and *Snake Poems*. His works have appeared in anthologies such as *Palabra Nueva: Cuentos Chicanos* and *Practicing Angels: Contemporary Anthology of San Francisco*. Alarcón received the 1989–1990 Writer's Fellowship from the California Arts Council. He now lives in San Francisco and is a professor at the University of California at Santa Cruz. Alarcón is also president of El Centro Chicano de Escritores, a nonprofit organization that promotes Chicano/Latino literary expression.

Julia Alvarez is originally from the Dominican Republic. She now lives in Vermont, where she teaches and writes. Her first book of poetry, *Homecoming*, was published in 1984. Alvarez has also written a book of short stories entitled *Daughters of Invention*.

Rosario Caicedo is a native of Colombia who now lives in Connecticut with her two children. Her poems have appeared in various publications and anthologies, including *Sinister Wisdom*, *Sojourner*, and *Embers*. Caicedo has recently completed work on her first book of poetry.

Rosemary Catacalos (1944–) was born in St. Petersburg, Florida, but grew up in San Antonio, Texas. As a child, she loved to read and began writing poetry and prose at an early age. Encouraged by a college professor, Catacalos pursued writing and published her first group of poems in 1970. For many years, she conducted poetry workshops for elementary- and secondary-school students in Texas. Catacalos is the author of *As Long as It Takes*, a book of poetry. Her collection of poems *Again for the First Time* received the Texas Institute of Letters Prize in Poetry in 1985. Catacalos directed the literature program at Guadalupe Cultural Arts Center in San Antonio. She is currently director of the Poetry Center at San Francisco State University.

Lorna Dee Cervantes (1954–) is an activist, editor, educator, and poet. A descendant of the Spanish families who first settled California, Cervantes experienced poverty and hardship as a child in San Jose. Growing up during the political and social unrest of the 1960s, she became involved in the Chicano movement while in high school. During her college years, Cervantes founded the literary magazine *Mango*, for a time printing it in her own kitchen. A graduate of San Jose State University, she has written two books of poetry, *Emplumada* and *From the Cables of Genocide: Poems on Love and Hunger*. Cervantes's Mexican American heritage plays a central role in her writing. She often focuses on the conflicts that arise from being caught between two cultures. Cervantes is the editor of *Red Dirt*, a magazine that focuses on multicultural literature. She currently teaches poetry at the University of Colorado.

Judith Ortiz Cofer (1952–) is a poet and novelist born in Puerto Rico. Her father was in the U.S. Navy, and as a child she lived in Puerto Rico and in various other parts of the United States. Cofer's writing contains the rich imagery of her culture. Her work has been published in many anthologies and distinguished journals. Her poetry book *Peregrina* won the

Riverstone Press International Poetry Competition in 1985. Cofer is also the author of two poetry collections, *Terms of Survival* and *Reaching for the Mainland*, a novel, *The Line of the Sun*, and a collection of personal essays and poems, *Silent Dancing*.

Victor Hernández Cruz (1949–) was born in Puerto Rico. When he was 5 years old, he moved to East Harlem in New York City with his family. His first volume of poetry was published when he was only 17. Among his books of poetry are *Snaps*, *Mainland*, *Tropicalization*, and *Rhythm, Content, and Flavor*. Cruz is among the most widely read Latino poets. His poetry is influenced by Latin and African American literature as well as by the African Caribbean music he heard as a boy. His poems portray the Puerto Rican experience in the United States and put readers in touch with the sounds and rhythms of the barrio. Cruz is the former editor of the publication *Umbra* and was a founder of the Gut Theater in New York. He has also been an instructor at San Francisco State University.

Martín Espada (1957–) was born in New York City and is of Puerto Rican descent. When his family moved from their Brooklyn neighborhood during his adolescence, his loneliness and isolation prompted him to begin writing. Espada studied at the University of Wisconsin and Northeastern University in Boston, where he received his law degree. As an attorney he has fought for the civil rights of immigrants and for bilingual education laws. Espada has received several awards and fellowships, and his poetry has been published in a number of magazines and anthologies. He is the author of *The Immigrant Iceboy's Bolero*, *Trumpets from the Islands of Their Eviction*, and *Rebellion Is the Circle of a Lover's Hands*.

Sandra María Esteves (1948–) was born in New York City and is the daughter of Puerto Rican and Dominican parents. Her first volume of poetry, *Yerba Buena*, gave voice to the urban Latina's experience. She is also the author of *Tropical Rains: A Bilingual Downpour* and *Bluestown Mockingbird Mambo*, which incorporates spiritual blues in its poetics. Esteves received a graduate degree from Pratt Institute in New York City and has exhibited her graphics widely. She was Artistic Director of the African Caribbean Poetry Theater. Esteves lives in New York City, where she actively promotes Latino literature.

Gustavo Pérez Firmat (1949–) was born in Havana, Cuba. His family immigrated to the United States in 1960, and he spent his adolescence in Miami. Firmat was educated at the University of Miami and the University of Michigan. His poems have been published in journals such as *The Bilingual Review/LaRevista Bilingue, Linden Lane,* and *Caribbean Review.* Firmat teaches Spanish and Spanish American Literature at Duke University and is working on a new collection of poetry.

Mario Garza We were unable to locate biographical information for this poet.

Carolina Hospital is a Cuban American writer of short fiction, essays, and poetry. She has been published in *The Americas Review, Linden Lane,* and *Caribbean Review.* Her writing also appeared in *Polyphony,* the first anthology of Cuban Americans writing in English. Hospital lives in Miami and teaches writing at Miami Dade Community College. She has completed her first book of poetry, *Letters Put Away.*

Tato Laviera (1959–) is among the most popular Latino poets in the United States today. He left Puerto Rico with his family in 1960 and grew up in a Spanish-speaking neighborhood of New York City. Laviera's poetry comes from a Latino oral tradition and combines the rhythms of Africa, the Caribbean, and Latin America. It often celebrates the existence of a true Latino culture within the United States. His latest volume of poetry is *Continental.* Earlier volumes include *The Enclave, AmeRícan,* and *Mainstream Ethics.* Laviera is also a playwright. He teaches drama and poetry at universities and conducts workshops in creative writing and drama for students of all ages.

Ben Luna is the author of an unpublished book of poetry, *Flowers for the Dead King of Mexico,* and has had many of his poems published in the *Chicano* Press. Luna has also written a television play. One of his life interests is painting, and he has painted murals in churches and auditoriums.

Belkis Cuza Malé (1942–) is the author of several books of poetry, including *Tiempo de sol* and *Women on the Front Lines.* She has also written two novels. Born in Cuba, she now lives in New Jersey with her husband, Cuban poet Heberto Padilla. Malé is the founder and editor of *Linden Lane Magazine,* which she and her husband publish.

Rita Mendoza is a Chicana poet. Her poem "Thoughts from a Chicana Woman," which is excerpted in this volume, won First Chicano Literary Prize from the University of California at Irvine in 1975.

Pat Mora (1942–) was born and raised in El Paso, Texas. She attended local schools and received her undergraduate and graduate degrees from the University of Texas at El Paso. Mora is the author of three collections of poetry: *Chants, Borders,* and *Journeys.* She has also written the children's book *Tomás and the Library Lady.* Mora's poetry addresses the Mexican American experience and has been influenced by her geographical surroundings. She sees the desert that extends from Mexico north to the Rocky Mountains as a common bond between two countries and two diverse cultures. Mora often emphasizes the harmony between Mexico and the United States. The rich heritage of Mexican Americans figures strongly in her work. Mora has received several prestigious awards, including two Southwest Book Awards for her first two volumes of poetry.

Aurora Levins Morales (1954–) was born in Puerto Rico and is the daughter of a Jewish father and a Puerto Rican mother. She grew up on a coffee farm in the mountains and was raised on "books and social justice." She began to write poetry when she was 7 years old. Her family eventually returned to the United States, where she was educated. Her work has been published in a number of anthologies. With her mother, Rosario Morales, she coauthored *Getting Home Alive,* a collection of poetry and prose that explores the lives of two Puerto Rican women. Aurora Levins Morales won the Oakland Arts Council Fellowship for her story "Vivir Para Ti" and has recently completed a collection of short stories.

Elías Miguel Muñoz (1954–) was sent to Spain in the late 1960s by his parents to escape the political unrest in Cuba. After spending eight months with relatives, he was able to join his parents who had moved to California. Muñoz learned English quickly and excelled in his classes. After college, he received a scholarship to study literature in Madrid, fulfilling his dream of returning to Spain. He later received a Ph.D. in Spanish from the University of California at Irvine. Muñoz taught Latin American literature at Wichita State University in Kansas but left to become a full-time writer of fiction and poetry. His writing often explores his childhood experiences in Cuba and Spain.

Richard Olivas We were unable to locate biographical information for this poet.

Ana Luisa Ortiz de Montellano was born in Mexico. Her father was a Mexican poet and her mother a British American teacher. Ortiz de Montellano finds that her mixed heritage influences her life in various ways. In one sense, she feels like an exile wherever she lives, but she also draws upon "a wide range of creative and cultural options."

Heberto Padilla (1932–) was born and raised in Cuba. He now lives in exile in the United States with his wife Belkis Cuza Malé, also a poet. Padilla's poems draw on his experiences in exile but are also inspired by the simple routines of daily life. Among his works are the poetry collections *Legacies* and *A Fountain, a House of Stone*. Padilla's memoir *Self-Portrait of the Other* discusses his arrest, imprisonment, and exile by the Communist government in Cuba. A former journalist and teacher, Padilla currently publishes the magazine *Linden Lane* with his wife.

Ricardo Pau-Llosa is a poet of Cuban descent. His works have appeared in various publications, including *New England Review, Iowa Review, Missouri Review, Denver Quarterly*, and *Crazyhorse*. Pau-Llosa is the author of *Bread of the Imagined*.

Antonia Quintana Pigño was born in Albuquerque, New Mexico. She is the author of a full-length epic poem, *La Jornada*, and a book of poems, *Poesias de 'La Jornado.'* Her work has also appeared in *The Latin American Review, The Bloomsbury Review, Encore, Southwest: A Contemporary Anthology*, and in other publications.

Naomi Quiñónez is the author of a collection of poetry entitled *Hummingbird Dreams*. She is also the coeditor of *Multicultural L.A.: An Anthology of Urban Poetry*, which received a Before Columbus Foundation American Book Award. Quiñónez lives in Los Angeles.

Leroy Quintana (1944–) has been strongly influenced by the oral tradition of his Mexican American culture. As a child growing up in New Mexico, he listened to the many traditional stories told by his grandparents. These stories first stirred his interest in being a storyteller. Quintana served in the U.S. Army during the Vietnam War and later graduated from the University of New Mexico. He worked as a social worker, a teacher, and a journalist. He has completed a collection of poems about his boyhood and is also working on short fiction, a novel, and a screenplay. Quintana is currently a professor of English at Mesa College in San Diego.

Luis Omar Salinas (1937–) was born in Texas and raised in California. As a youth he was an avid reader and knew he wanted to become a writer. After high school Salinas worked at various odd jobs while taking classes at several California colleges. At Fresno State University he served as the editor of *Backwash*, a university literary magazine, and was active in the Chicano movement on campus. Salinas's first collection of poetry, *Crazy Gypsy*, was published in 1971. During the 1970s, Salinas coedited the Chicano anthology *From the Barrio* and published several poems in the collection *Entrance: 4 Chicano Poets*. His poems have appeared in other anthologies, journals, and newspapers. Today Salinas continues to write while working as a Spanish translator.

Gary Soto (1952–) was born in Fresno, California. He is a graduate of California State University and the University of California at Irvine, where he studied creative writing. Soto has published seven collections of poetry, including *Black Hair, A Fire in My Hands*, and *Who Will Know Us?* His first book of poetry, *The Elements of San Joaquin*, won the 1976 United States Award of the International Poetry Forum. Soto's poetry is known for its clear, powerful images and often deals with the harsh realities of Mexican American life. Factory work and farm labor are part of the rich but sometimes painful personal history that he draws upon in his writing. Soto teaches Chicano Studies and English at the University of California at Berkeley.

Ricardo Vásquez We were unable to locate biographical information for this poet.

Marisella Veiga was born in Havana, Cuba. Her family immigrated to the United States in 1960. She grew up in St. Paul, Minnesota, and Miami, Florida, and received a degree in creative writing from Bowling Green State University in Ohio. Veiga has worked in Puerto Rico as a business writer and as an international news reporter. Her poetry has been published in several literary magazines. She now works as an editor and translator for an international publication.

Alma Luz Villanueva (1944–) makes her home in Santa Cruz, California. She has written several books of poetry, including *Bloodroot* and *Life Span*. Villanueva's first novel, *The Ultraviolet Sky*, received a Before Columbus Foundation American Book Award. She has also completed a second novel, *Naked Ladies*, and a new book of poetry, *Planet*.

Bernice Zamora (1938–) was born and raised in Colorado, where her ancestors were among the first Spanish settlers. She received her undergraduate and graduate degrees from universities in Colorado and later a Ph.D. in English from Stanford University in California. Zamora is the author of a book of poems, *Restless Serpents*. Her poetry has also been published in a variety of literary magazines and anthologies. Social and political causes are often the subjects of her work. Zamora teaches English at Santa Clara University in California.

GLOSSARY

A

ambidextrous (am-buh-DEHKS-truhs) having the ability to use both hands with equal ease; very skillful (44)

apparition (ap-uh-RIHSH-uhn) ghostlike figure (63)

arid (AR-ihd) dry and barren (15)

aristocracy (ar-ih-STAH-kruh-see) superior group or class; government by a privileged minority or upper class (6)

B

Babylon (BAB-uh-luhn) ancient city on the Euphrates river; the capital of Babylonia, famous for wealth, luxury, and wickedness (51)

bamboo (bam-BOO) woody tropical plant of the grass family with hollow, jointed stems, used for making fishing poles, canes, and furniture (16)

bicameral (beye-KAM-uhr-uhl) pertaining to or consisting of two legislative chambers (44)

Bronx (BRAHNGKS) northernmost borough of New York City (68)

Buddha (BŌŌD-uh) Siddhartha Gautama, a religious philosopher and teacher who lived in India during the sixth century B.C. and was the founder of Buddhism (62)

burrowed (BER-ohd) hidden; dug deeply (16)

C

caboose (kuh-BOOS) last car of a freight train (62)

caravan (KAR-uh-van) group of people or vehicles traveling together for safety (66)

Chichimec (CHEE-chee-mehk) Indian civilization of Mexico that flourished prior to the arrival of the Spanish in the early 1500s (79)

commences (kuh-MEHNS-ihs) begins (83)

Con Edison shortened form of Consolidated Edison, a major utility company in New York (82)

conjuring (KAHN-juhr-ihng) using magic to call or summon somebody or something; calling to mind (21)

Corpus Christi (KOHR-puhs KRIHS-tee) city in southeastern Texas (66)

corsairs (KAWR-serz) pirates (39)

D

Delano (duh-LAYN-oh) the town in Central California in which César Chávez and agricultural workers first formed labor unions in the late 1960s and early l970s (8)

diatribes (DEYE-uh-treyebz) bitter criticisms or denunciations (12)

divine (duh-VEYEN) predict (21)

E

East Harlem (HAHR-luhm) northeast section of New York City (16)

ebony (EHB-uh-nee) black in color, like ebony wood (42)

entrails (EHN-traylz) innner organs of humans or animals; inner parts of something (4)

epidemics (ehp-uh-DEHM-ihks) contagious diseases affecting great numbers of people in a community at the same time (27)

F

finite (FEYE-neyet) having limits or bounds; not too great or too small to be measured (75)

flail (FLAYL) strike or beat as with a flail, an instrument used to thresh grain by hand (22)

Formica (fawr-MEYE-kuh) trademark for a laminated, heat-resistant plastic used for furniture, counters, sinks, and so on (20)

frayed (FRAYD) ragged (66)

H

heady (HEHD-ee) intoxicating; strong in odor (20)

hoax (HOHKS) trick or practical joke (22)

I

impose (ihm-POHZ) place or set (12)

incantations (ihn-can-TAY-shuhnz) chanting of certain words in order to cast a spell (69)

ingenious (ihn-JEEN-yuhs) clever, resourceful, inventive (39)

intrigue (ihn-TREEG) awaken the curiosity or interest of (38)

J

justification (jus-tuh-fih-KAY-shuhn) reason, explanation (85)

K

karma (KAHR-muh) destiny or fate (69)

King's English standard or accepted English usage in speech or writing (32)

L

Long Island island in southeast New York (52)

lyrically (LIHR-ih-kuhl-lee) expressing deep personal feelings in a musical way (20)

M

maestro (MEYES-troh) master in any art, especially music (6)

mantra (MAN-truh) word or series of words chanted as a prayer (62)

masculinity (mas-kyoo-LIHN-ih-tee) manliness; the quality of being like a man (85)

matriarch (MAY-tree-ahrk) mother who rules her family or tribe (60)

mosaic (moh-ZAY-ihk) design or picture created by inlaying small pieces of variously colored enamel, glass, precious stones, or the like in mortar (66)

multivocal (mul-tih-VOH-kuhl) word invented by the author to mean having many voices (44)

N

nostalgia (nahs-TAL-juh) homesickness or a longing for a previous time (71)

O

oblong (AHB-lawng) rectangular in shape and longer in one direction than another (65)

Olmec (OHL-mehk) one of the ancient Indian civilizations of Mexico known for its large stone carvings (79)

omnipossibilist (ahm-nih-PAHS-uh-buhl-ihst) word invented by the author to mean a person who sees possibilities everywhere (44)

operetta (ahp-uhr-EHT-uh) light, amusing opera with spoken dialogue (62)

P

Patroness of Exiles (PAY-truhn-ihs . . . EHKS-eyelz) saint, invented by the author, who looks after and protects people who no longer live in their own land (20)

Phoenician (fih-NIHSH-uhn) ancient civilization of the Middle East (78)

plantains (PLAN-tihnz) tropical banana plants whose fruits are eaten as cooked vegetables (20)

prefabricated (pree-FAB-rih-kayt-uhd) manufactured or constructed beforehand or in standardized parts for rapid assembly (69)

prima donna (PREE-muh DAHN-uh) principle woman singer in an opera or concert; vain, temperamental person (62)

profusion (proh-FYOO-zhuhn) rich supply (24)

Purple Heart decoration awarded to soldiers wounded in action against an enemy (30)

Q

quasar (KWAY-zahr) distant celestial object that gives off large quantities of light, radio waves, or both (63)

R

railroad flat apartment of rooms in a line, entered one from another, with no hallway (62)

reiterate (ree-IHT-uh-rayt) repeat (83)

repatriating (ree-PAY-tree-ayt-ihng) returning people to the countries of their birth, citizenship, or allegiance (43)

repertoire (REHP-uhr-twahr) list of dramas, operas, or other works that can be performed by a person or company (69)

reproach (rih-PROHCH) expression of blame; criticism (38)

Robstown town in southern Texas (10)

S

scythe (SEYETH) tool with long, curving blade and long handle used for cutting grass and grain (4)

sickle (SIHK-uhl) tool with crescent-shaped blade and short handle used for cutting tall grass and weeds (4)

siren (SEYE-ruhn) in Greek mythology, a sea nymph, represented as part bird and part woman, who, by singing, led sailors to their deaths on rocky coasts (63)

skeletal (SKEHL-uh-tuhl) referring to shape or form; like a skeleton (32)

sluggish (SLUG-ihsh) lacking energy or alertness; slow moving (4)

sonatas (suh-NAHT-uhs) musical works for one or two instruments (69)

spic (SPIHK) derogatory slang term used to describe someone with a Latino background (37)

T

testimonies (TEHS-tuh-moh-neez) evidence given in support of a fact or statement; proof; open declarations of faith (66)

Toltec (TAHL-tehk) ancient group of Nahuatl Indians who lived in Mexico before the Aztec (79)

V

valor (VAL-uhr) marked courage or bravery (85)

vigil (VIHJ-uhl) period of watchful attention (63)

void (VOID) empty space (75)

votive (VOHT-ihv) given; dedicated (20)

W

whorls (WHAWRLZ) things with coiled or spiral appearance (24)

winter solstice time in the Northern Hemisphere when the sun is farthest from the equator; December 21 or 22 (34)

INDEX OF POETS

ACKNOWLEDGMENTS

Globe Fearon wishes to thank the following copyright owners for permission to reproduce poetry in this book:

ARTE PUBLICO PRESS, University of Houston, for Lorna Dee Cervantes, "The Beauty of Me and My People" and "Which Line Is This? I Forget" from *Kikiriki, Stories and Poems in English and Spanish for Children*, edited by Sylvia Cavazos Peña, 1981. Judith Ortiz Cofer, "Mamacita" from *Terms of Survival*. Copyright © 1987 Judith Ortiz Cofer; "The Latin Deli" from *Decade II: A Twentieth Anniversary Anthology*, edited by Julián Oliveras and Evangelina Vigil-Piñón. Victor Hernández Cruz, "Side 12" and "Side 32" from *Rhythm, Content and Flavor*. Copyright © 1989 Victor Hernández Cruz. Sandra María Esteves, "Father's Day on Longwood Avenue" and "Religious Instructions for Young Casualties" from *Bluestown Mockingbird Mambo*. Copyright © 1990 Sandra María Esteves. Carolina Hospital, "Dear Tía" from *Decade II: An Anniversary Anthology*, edited by Julián Oliveras and Evangelina Vigil-Piñón. Reprinted by permission from the publisher of *The Americas Review* vol.17, no. 1, 1989. Tato Laviera, "jíbaro" from *AmeRícan*. Copyright © 1985 Tato Laviera. Pat Mora, "Lesson 1," "Lesson 2" and "Elena," from *Chants*. Copyright © 1984 Pat Mora; "Immigrants" from *Borders*, 1986. Luis Omar Salinas, "Sweet Drama" from *Decade II: An Anniversary Anthology*, edited by Julián Oliveras and Evangelina Vigil-Piñón. Reprinted by permission from the publisher of *The Americas Review* vol.20, no.1, 1992. **SUSAN BERGHOLZ LITERARY SERVICES**, New York, for Julia Alvarez, "Ironing Their Clothes" from *Homecoming*. Copyright © 1984 by Julia Alvarez. First published in *The Renewal of the Vision: Voices of Latin American Women Poets*, edited by Marjorie Agosin and Cola Frangen, Spectacular Diseases, 1987. Reprinted by permission. **BILINGUAL PRESS/EDITORIAL BILINGUE**, Arizona State University, Tempe, for Judith Ortiz Cofer, "My Father in the Navy: A Childhood Memory" from her collection *Reaching for the Mainland*, appearing in Triple Crown, 1987. Copyright © 1987 Bilingual Press/Editorial Bilingue. Martín Espada, "Tony Went to the Bodega but He Didn't Buy Anything" and "We Live by What We See at Night" from *Trumpets from the Islands of their Eviction*. Copyright © 1987 Bilingual Press/Editorial Bilingue. Gustavo Pérez Firmat, "Home" from his collection *Carolina Cuban*, appearing in Triple Crown, 1987. Elías Miguel Muñoz, "Returning," "Little Has Been Written About Cowards," and "Little Sister Born in This Land" from *En estas tierras/In This Land*. Bernice Zamora, "Pueblo Winter" from *Releasing Serpents*. Previously published in *Restless Serpents* by Bernice Zamora. Copyright © 1993 by Bernice Zamora. **ROSARIO CAICEDO**, "Nochebuena" from *Looking for Home, Women Writing About Exile* (Minneapolis: Milkweed Editions). Copyright © 1990. Reprinted by permission of the author. **CANFIELD PRESS**, for Luis Omar Salinas, "In a Farmhouse" and "Mestizo," Leonard Adamé, "My Grandmother Would Rock Quietly and Hum," and Ben Luna, "Los Angeles" from *From the Barrio: A Chicano Anthology*, edited by Luis Omar Salinas and Lillian Faderman. Copyright © 1973 Luis Omar Salinas and Lillian Faderman. **CANTO AL PUEBLO NATIONAL BOARD**, for Mario Garza, "Mi Padre" and "Applying for a Civil Service Job" from *Canto al Pueblo: An Anthology of Experiences*. Copyright © 1978 by Canto al Pueblo National Board. Globe Fearon has executed a reasonable and concerted effort to contact Canto al Pueblo National Board. We eagerly invite any persons knowledgeable about the whereabouts of the author or agent to contact Globe Fearon to arrange for the customary publishing transactions. **CAPRA PRESS**, for Teresa Paloma Acosta,